The Last Days of Steam in
BRISTOL AND
SOMERSET

To my dear Mother who has spent so much time assisting with my writing

THE LAST DAYS OF STEAM IN
BRISTOL AND SOMERSET

— COLIN G. MAGGS —

ALAN SUTTON

First published in the United Kingdom in 1992
Alan Sutton Publishing Ltd · Phoenix Mill · Far Thrupp · Stroud · Gloucestershire

First published in the United States of America in 1992
Alan Sutton Publishing Inc. · Wolfeboro Falls · NH 03896–0848

British Library Cataloguing in Publication Data

Maggs, Colin G. (Colin Gordon), *1932–*
  The last days of steam in Bristol and Somerset.
  I. Title
  625.26109423

  ISBN 0-7509-0001-6

Library of Congress Cataloging in Publication Data applied for

Jacket illustrations:
Front: BR Standard class 4MT 4–6–0 No. 75071 on 9.9.61 lifts SR 3-coach set No. 397
out of Midford working the 4.35 p.m. Bath–Templecombe.
Back: Ex-LMS Ivatt class 2MT 2–6–2T No. 41245, of Bristol St Philip's Marsh shed, at
Yatton on 22.8.62 having arrived from Bristol with empty stock form the 2.45 p.m.
Yatton–Witham. The letters 'SC' below the number on the door, indicate that the
smokebox was self-cleaning. This meant that the ash was blown through the chimney
rather than accumulating inside. This type of smokebox prevented the emission of
sparks, as by the time the ash had passed through a wire-net screen, the ashes were
small, dead and harmless.

Typeset in 9/10 Palatino
Typesetting and origination by
Alan Sutton Publishing Limited.
Printed in Great Britain by
The Bath Press, Bath, Avon.

Introduction

Somerset is a county of varied topography – rolling hills in the north and south with flat moors between. Its railways were also varied. Pre-nationalization saw the Great Western Railway serving most of the county, although there was a main line of the London, Midland and Scottish Railway in the north and the Southern Railway in the south. These two companies were linked by the Somerset and Dorset Joint Railway on its route to and from Bournemouth. The Weston, Clevedon and Portishead Light Railway unfortunately closed in 1940.

The last days of steam in the BR era saw this pattern largely unchanged, with ex-GWR, LMS, SR and S&DJR engines still running. The BR standard classes, with the exception of the 'Clan' Pacifics, could also be seen and an ex-LNER 'B1' class 4–6–0 put in an appearance on the ex-LMS lines.

Closure of the steam locomotive depots was protracted. The former GWR shed at Bristol, Bath Road, was the first major depot in the area to close to steam in 1960. Bristol, St Philip's Marsh and Taunton followed in 1964, while Barrow Road, the only remaining Bristol shed to service steam locomotives, closed the following year. Main-line steam in the area came to an end on 7 March 1966 with the closure of Bath Green Park and Templecombe sheds resulting from the withdrawal of services on the Somerset and Dorset line.

The first pictures in this volume cover Bristol followed by those of the original county of Somerset, starting from the north and working southwards. There are also photographs of industrial lines, in which the county was surprisingly rich, and enthusiasts' specials.

Most of the pictures have never been reproduced before, the very few which have being well worth repeating. The aim has been to offer to the reader as wide a variety of scene and locomotive power as possible.

Photographs without a credit were taken by the author.

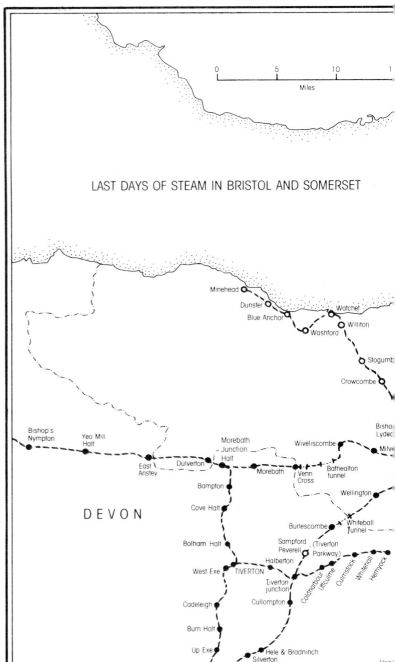

LAST DAYS OF STEAM IN BRISTOL AND SOMERSET

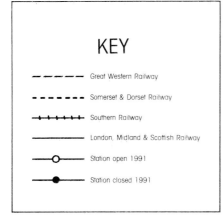

KEY

– – – – – Great Western Railway

▪ ▪ ▪ ▪ ▪ Somerset & Dorset Railway

+–+–+–+–+ Southern Railway

———— London, Midland & Scottish Railway

—○— Station open 1991

—●— Station closed 1991

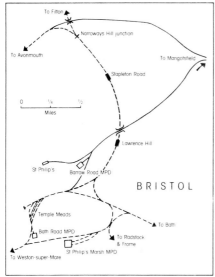

BRISTOL

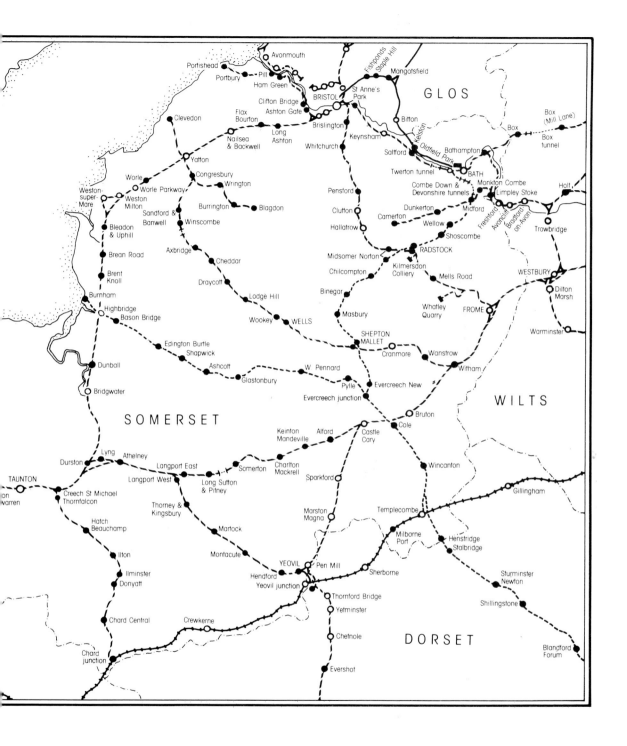

Acknowledgements

Grateful thanks are due to Hugh Ballantyne, John Cornelius, S.P.J.A. Derek and R.E. Toop for allowing the author access to their photographs and to John Hayward for checking and improving the captions.

Variety at Bristol Temple Meads on 14.6.58: ex-LMS class 5 4–6–0 No. 45265 of Saltley shed has arrived at platform 4 with a North–West express, and ex-GWR 43XX class 2–6–0 No. 6399 from Westbury shed is running light engine. Floodlamps illuminate the loco yard of Bath Road shed on the right of the photograph. Spotters abound.

R.E. Toop

No. 45265 is still at platform 4 on 14.6.58 and 45XX class 2–6–2T No. 5529 propels two locomotives, one being BR Standard class 4MT 4–6–0 No. 75000.

R.E. Toop

Spotters climb on the footplate of 43XX class 2–6–0 No. 6384 and 'Modified Hall' No. 6972 *Beningbrough Hall* on an unknown date. Although the loco yard is lit by electric floodlights, the station platform still has a gas lamp, this form of illumination remaining until as late as 1960.

R.E. Toop

BR Standard class 5MT No. 73092 reversing out of Temple Meads on 14.4.62. The semaphore on the gantry signal (far right) controlled shunting movements in Bristol goods depot. The lines beyond the fence are both goods roads, the nearer one leading to Bristol Harbour. Milepost $118\frac{1}{4}$ stands at the end of platform 9 and indicates the mileage from Paddington via Box.

LMS and BR Standard class 5MT 4–6–0s No. 44965 and No. 73068 at Temple Meads platform 9 with the northbound 'Devonian' having taken over from a Western Region engine on 18.5.59. Temple Meads goods depot is behind the locos, the vans indicating the severe 'Down' gradient to reach it.
John Cornelius

4–6–0 No. 5011 *Tintagel Castle* of Newton Abbot shed arrives at Temple Meads with a West–North express on 18.5.59.

John Cornelius

'Castle' class No. 4037 *The South Wales Borderers* of Newton Abbot shed, heads an 'Up' express at platform 9 on 18.5.59, while an Ivatt class 2 2–6–2T stands on an adjoining line.

John Cornelius

No. 4037 *The South Wales Borderers* at Temple Meads on 18.5.59. In the right foreground notice the water crane with a 'devil' which was lit in cold weather to prevent freezing. Between them is the handle to operate the water valve. Lying near the foot of the water crane is a spare coupling.

John Cornelius

'Black Five' No. 45335, with stock for the 9.15 a.m. stopping train to Gloucester, standing on one of the centre carriage roads in Brunel's terminus waiting to pull into platform 12 on 9.6.62. Note the plume of steam blowing off from the safety valves in the confines under the old station roof and at 225 lb per square inch this could be a deafening experience. Notice also the timber-built platform to the right of the engine.

Ex-LNER B1 class 4–6–0 No. 61167 of Mexborough shed leaving Temple Meads platform 9 with a Paignton–Bradford train on 17.8.63. A 4–6–0 'County' stands just outside the train shed.

Hugh Ballantyne

Ex-LNER B1 class 4–6–0 No. 61137 and BR Standard Class 5MT 4–6–0 No. 73019 leaving Brunel's terminal train shed, Temple Meads, to proceed to Barrow Road MPD on 6.8.63.

Barrow Road MPD, Bristol, on 19.4.65. An ex-LMS depot, it latterly stabled ex-Western Region engines when Bath Road and St Philip's Marsh depots closed to steam. Left to right: class 8F 2–8–0 No. 48409, a steam crane and BR Standard class 5MT No. 73003 shedded at Barrow Road. Most of the engines beyond are ex-GWR. Beyond the bridge is the coaling tower.

R.E. Toop

Class 5MT 4–6–0 No. 45264 of Northampton outside Barrow Road shed on 21.3.65. Wagon turntables can be seen in front of the bogie and below the rear set of coupled wheels.

John Cornelius

4–6–0 No. 7029 *Clun Castle*, now owned by Birmingham Railway Museum, at Barrow Road shed on 21.3.65.

John Cornelius

BR Standard class 3MT 2–6–2T No. 82040 of Bristol Bath Road shed arrives at Stapleton Road on the 'Up' relief line with a train to Severn Beach on 22.8.59. The 'B' headlamp code is in the alternative position on the buffer beam, frequently practised but unorthodox. Notice the PA system fixed to the concrete lamp-posts and the length of the 'Up' main signal arm compared with that for the relief.

John Cornelius

Grubby-looking No. 6950 *Kingsthorpe Hall* climbs the 1 in 75 gradient past Narroways Hill junction with an express in May 1963. The Clifton Extension Line to Avonmouth and Severn Beach curves to the right.

W.H. Harbor/author's collection

No. 4903 *Astley Hall* heads an 'Up' mixed freight approaching Oldfield Park on 30.12.63. The first 4 wagons are empty hopper ballast wagons, followed by 9 loaded coal trucks, 2 fuel tankers, 2 open wagons and more loaded coal wagons.

R.E. Toop

2–8–2T No. 7209 in May 1963 at Narroways Hill junction climbing the 1 in 75 gradient with empty wagons, probably destined for the South Wales coalfield. Notice the catch point on this 'Up' relief line protecting the junction from runaways.

W.H. Harbor/author's collection

BR Standard class 9F 2–10–0 No. 92242 with empty wagon train at Narroways Hill junction in May 1963.

W.H. Harbor/author's collection

No. 7811 *Dunley Manor* leaves Twerton tunnel west of Bath, with a 'Down' goods on 13.2.63. Snow from the Big Freeze still abounds. Until 1950 a refuge siding, controlled by Twerton tunnel signal-box, was located to the right of the loco.

Diesel-hydraulic D7039 and 4–6–0 No. 6907 *Davenham Hall* head the 4.25 p.m. Cardiff–Portsmouth near Twerton tunnel on 22.6.63. Diesel locos were usually coupled in front, rather than behind, a steam engine to avoid their ventilating fans sucking dirt into the machinery.

No. 7923 *Speke Hall* of Southall shed approaches Bath with an 'Up' express on 22.8.59. Bullhead rail on the 'Up' road has just been replaced by the flat-bottomed variety. Products of Stothert and Pitt's crane works can be seen in the background.

John Cornelius

No. 1000 *County of Middlesex* of Bristol Bath Road shed, heads an 'Up' parcels train on 2.3.63 past the vandalized Twerton tunnel signal-box which closed on 20.11.60 as a result of the Bristol Multiple Aspect Signalling being brought into operation. In the rear of three 6-wheel milk tanks, coded 'MILTA', is a Royal Mail van.

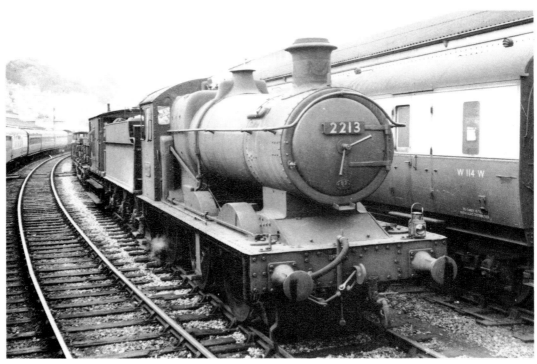

2251 class 0–6–0 No. 2213 of Bristol St Philip's Marsh shed stands on 28.6.59 at Bath Spa on one of the middle roads with an engineer's train. To the right of the smokebox is passenger brake van W114W built at Swindon in 1934 under Lot 1512.

John Cornelius

Ex-GWR 28XX 2–8–0 No. 3804 heads a train, probably a pigeon special, at Newton Meadows, west of Bath, on the former LMS Mangotsfield to Bath line on 8.8.59. This was the first known appearance of this class on the branch.

Class 8F 2–8–0 No. 48737 of Bath Green Park shed heads a Bath–Birmingham freight into the evening sunshine below Kelston Park on 16.6.64.

BR Standard class 3MT 2–6–2T No. 82033 from Bath Road shed passes Bath junction with the 6.18 p.m. Bath Green Park–Bristol Temple Meads on 14.8.59. Ex-Somerset and Dorset class 4F 0–6–0 No. 44559 is to the left.

Ex-Somerset and Dorset class 4F 0–6–0 No. 44558 being manually turned on the table at Bath Green Park shed on 7.6.64. BR Standard Class 9F 2–10–0 No. 92214, now preserved at the Midland Railway Centre, Butterley, stands in front of the water tanks.

Class 3F 0–6–0T No. 47552 on 7.6.64 at Bath MPD with snow plough.

Ex-GWR 57XX class 0–6–0PT No. 3742 on 7.6.64 at the foot of the water softening plant, Bath MPD. The old tender containing sludge is lettered: 'To be returned to the water softening plant Bath'.

'Jubilee' class No. 45594 *Bhopal* stands near the turntable at Bath in July 1961. The timber-built Somerset and Dorset engine shed is on the left, and the stone-built Midland Railway shed lies behind the tender. Notice the gas lamp.

Revd Alan Newman

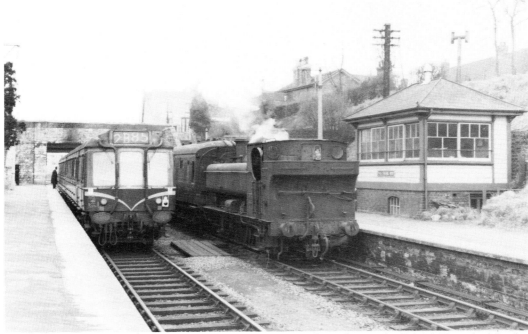

57XX class 0–6–0PT No. 7729 working the 1.00 p.m. Saturdays-only Bristol Temple Meads–Portishead crosses dmu Nos. W55032 and W56292 working the 1.15 p.m. Portishead–Temple Meads at Pill on 17.2.62. Notice the fire irons on the bunker of the Pannier tank.

Hugh Ballantyne

14XX class 0–4–2T No. 1463 of Yatton shed at Yatton backing off wagons from the 10.30 a.m. mixed train from Clevedon on 13.6.57.

14XX class 0–4–2T No. 1412 propelling the 3.45 p.m. Clevedon–Yatton away from the terminus on 30.8.58. The goods shed is on the right.

R.E. Toop

14XX class 0–4–2T No. 1463 of Yatton shed standing in the Clevedon bay platform at Yatton on Easter Monday 1957. Driver George Hunt is shaking hands with W.E. Harbor, formerly a checker at Clevedon goods depot, while station-master W.G. Saunders looks on in the background.

W.H. Harbour/author's collection

Ex-LMS Ivatt class 2MT 2–6–2T No. 41245 of Bristol St Philip's Marsh shed at Yatton having arrived from Bristol with empty stock to form the 2.45 p.m. Yatton–Witham on 22.8.62. Its tanks are being filled with water from the 'mushroom'-pattern storage tank. Notice the 'egg-cup' into which the leather filler bag is placed after use so that any drips may be caught. On completion of watering, the headlamps will be changed by the fireman.

45XX class 2–6–2T No. 5528 approaches Congresbury on 13.6.57 with the 7.25 a.m. Bristol–Witham and Frome.

57XX class 0–6–0PT No. 3696 leaves Congresbury on 22.10.62 with a 'Down' goods train. The small arm on the bracket signal is for the Wrington branch.

Having taken empty hopper wagons to Banwell, ex-LMS Ivatt class 2MT No. 41208 and brake van return to Congresbury on 22.10.62 and will now work the Wrington Vale goods.

BR Standard class 3MT 2–6–2T No. 82035 arrives at Axbridge on 2.7.60 with the 1.27 p.m. Saturdays-only Yatton–Wells comprised of two 'B' sets.

R.E. Toop

BR Standard class 3MT 2–6–2T No. 82039 arriving at Wookey with the 11.12 a.m. Yatton–Witham on 17.3.62. The nearest building on the platform is the signal-box, closed by this date, access to the sidings being given by a ground frame. A Tilley pressure lamp hangs from the nearest concrete lamp standard.

R.E. Toop

Ivatt class 2MT No. 41245 of Bristol St Philip's Marsh shed at Wells with the 2.45 p.m. Yatton–Witham on 22.8.62. The engine carries the lower position 'B' headlamp. The water crane and its accompanying features can be seen while beyond a private siding curves left into Messrs A. Sheldon's premises. Notice the solitary upper quadrant signal to the left of the bracket signals. The former was controlled from the Somerset and Dorset ground frame.

57XX class 0–6–0PT No. 9612 on 17.3.62 is near Wells East Somerset signal-box with a 'Down' pick-up freight.

R.E. Toop

The fireman of Ivatt class 2MT 2–6–2T No. 41245 working the 2.45 p.m. Yatton–Witham hands the tablet to the Shepton Mallet signalman on 22.8.62. 57XX class 0–6–0PT No. 4607 waits at the platform with the 3.28 p.m. Witham–Yatton.

BR Standard class 3MT 2–6–2T No. 82040 leaves Shepton Mallet High Street on 6.4.63 with the 3.17 p.m. Saturdays-only Frome–Yatton.

R.E. Toop

57XX class 0–6–0PT No. 3748 at Shepton Mallet High Street on 31.3.59 with the 11.35 a.m. Yatton–Witham. The driver is calling to the photographer, 'Now then, smile!'

R.E. Toop

45XX class 2–6–2T No. 5523 stands at the mini train shed at Witham on 22.8.57 with the 7.25 a.m. Bristol–Witham and Frome, while a connecting main-line 'Up' train calls. The bay signal beyond the train shed is off for the reversal prior to entering the 'Up' platfom and subsequent departure to Frome. The GWR monogram on the footbridge is worth a second glance.

Ivatt class 2MT 2–6–2T No. 41208 from Bristol St Philip's Marsh shed, leaves Congresbury on 22.10.62 with the Wrington Vale goods. The fireman has forgotten to place a headlamp. The track here is carried on Second World War concrete pot sleepers tied to gauge at intervals. These were used on sidings and relief lines when wood was short, freeing the scarce timber sleepers for main-line use.

Ivatt class 2MT 2–6–2T No. 41208 passes the ungated Irwood Lane level crossing when returning from Wrington to Congresbury on 22.10.62. The track on this section of the branch is flat-bottomed rail spiked directly to the sleepers.

14XX class 0–4–2T No. 1412 at the ungated Irwood Lane crossing on 13.6.57.

57XX class 0–6–0PT No. 7772 taking on water at Bristol St Philip's Marsh shed on 12.4.61 prior to working a goods to Radstock. Fireman Hathaway supervises the operation. The chain is used for swinging the arm of the water crane.

Driver Denman and Fireman Hathaway on 57XX class 0–6–0PT No. 7772 at Radstock on 12.4.61. The 'C' above the number-plate is on a yellow disc, the 'C' indicating the power class and yellow the route restriction.

57XX class 0–6–0PT No. 9668 arrives at Brislington on 28.3.59 with a Temple Meads–Frome train. In the foreground are folded wagon tarpaulins. Notice the rods supporting the platform canopy. The Marsh junction distant signal can just be seen under the road overbridge.

R.E. Toop

45XX class 2–6–2T No. 5536 leaves Brislington with the 10.50 a.m. Frome–Temple Meads on 24.10.59. The coal yard is busy in this scene as the photograph was taken before the days when most homes were heated by gas or electricity.

Hugh Ballantyne

51XX class 2–6–2T No. 4131 passes Radstock West with a 'Down' empty wagon train on 14.8.59. This Bristol and North Somerset Railway station, like that at Brislington, also has its canopy supported.

View of a train at Hallatrow through the cab window of 57XX class 0–6–0PT No. 7772 on 12.4.61. Notice the GWR monogram and the smoke deflector on the footbridge.

BR Standard class 3MT 2–6–2T No. 82040 entering Mells Road on 4.4.59 with the 10.50 a.m. Frome–Temple Meads.

R.E. Toop

57XX class 0–6–0PT No. 5767 collecting rails and chairs on 28.5.58 following the lifting of the Camerton branch. This line, formerly serving collieries, featured in the film *The Titfield Thunderbolt*.

The same train has arrived at Monkton Combe with loaded wagons on 28.5.58 to propel empties back to the railhead to be loaded with more materials.

No. 5767 at Monkton Combe on 28.5.58 with empty wagons. The ironwork of the footbridge, just visible in the background, was cast at Paulton in 1811 and formerly spanned the Somerset Coal Canal on the same site.

Working tender first, 2251 class 0–6–0 No. 2217, on the left of the photograph, enters Frome with the 11.40 a.m. Weymouth–Frome on 19.4.63. The 1.05 p.m. Westbury–Weymouth dmu is to the right. The train shed, though now only served by a single track, is still extant.

SR class U 2–6–0 No. 31639 on the turntable at Bath Green Park MPD on 2.1.66 before working back light over the Somerset and Dorset. It had arrived on an enthusiasts' train. The notice behind the crew turning the engine warns that great care must be taken to see that an engine does not foul wagons on the coal stage road.

Bath Green Park shed on 5.3.66 with SR Light Pacifics No. 34006 *Bude* and No. 34057 *Biggin Hill*.

Ex-S&D class 7F 2–8–0 No. 53809 on 14.10.62 at Bath, its home shed. It is now at the Midland Railway Centre, Butterley. Behind it is a class 8F 2–8–0. Behind the 7F's chimney is the water softener.

John Cornelius

At Bath shed the last surviving Johnson class 1P 0–4–4T No. 58086 on 14.10.62, after withdrawal, awaits its call for scrapping. In the early days of the S&D this type worked most passenger trains and also those on the Mangotsfield to Bath line. Since the late forties they were normally only seen on the S&D south of the Mendip Hills. Stothert and Pitt cranes are in the background and class 2P 4–4–0 No. 40697 stands on the right.

John Cornelius

Ex-S&D class 2P 4–4–0 No. 40634 of Templecombe shed, and BR Standard class 9F 2–10–0 No. 92006 approach Bath with the 'Up' Pines Express on 31.7.61. The S&D used an individual headlamp code: passenger trains had a lamp by the chimney and right-hand buffer; freight trains had a lamp by the chimney and left-hand buffer.

John Cornelius

Class 2MT 2–6–2T No. 41307 and BR Standard class 4MT 2–6–4T No. 80138 arrive at Bath on 5.3.66 with the 14.00 Templecombe–Bath on the last day of scheduled working over the S&D.

Apart from the very last years when BR Standard class 4MT 2–6–4Ts took over some workings, tank engines were a rare sight on passenger trains on the northern section of the S&D, apart from this train, the 6.05 p.m. Bath Green Park–Binegar, photographed here on 14.8.59. Class 2MT 2–6–2T No. 41243 has just passed Bath junction signal-box.

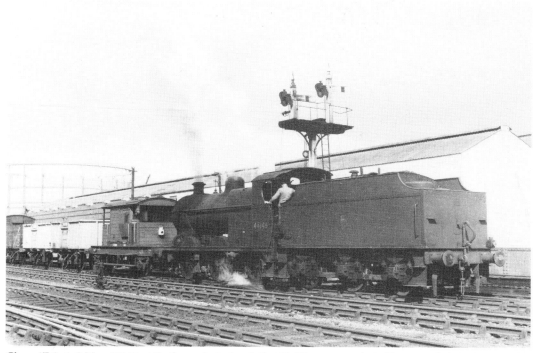

Class 4F 0–6–0 No. 44146 at Bath ready to bank the 11.00 a.m. goods to Evercreech junction up the 1 in 50 gradient to Combe Down tunnel on 5.9.60. The brake van is of SR design.

As BR Standard class 4MT 2–6–4T No. 80041 is not fitted with a tablet catcher, the driver of the 16.05 on 1.7.65 Wincanton–Bath hands the tablet manually to the Bath junction signalman on 1.7.65.

BR Standard class 5MT No. 73049 works an express unassisted up the 1 in 50 gradient from Bath junction on 28.3.59.

Class 4F 0–6–0 No. 44135 is not fitted with a tablet catcher so the fireman dangerously hangs on to grab the tablet pouch from the lineside apparatus, at the end of the timber walkway, from the signal-box on 28.3.59. Had the signalman been informed that the engine was not equipped with a catcher, he would have placed the tablet in a pouch with a larger handle.

Signalmen at Bath junction box were susceptible to colds through having to make frequent journeys into the fresh air to either set up or collect a tablet. Bath junction was unique among S&D single-line boxes in having to deal with a banking engine staff.

No. 44135 is hauling SR coach set 447. This was in its last weeks of service as it was withdrawn by July 1959.

Class 2P 4–4–0 No. 40537 and BR Standard class 5MT 4–6–0 No. 73019 climbing the 1 in 50 gradient away from Bath junction with the 'Down' Pines Express on 28.3.59.

Class 4F 0–6–0 No. 44146 (see the top photograph on p. 55) is dropping off the 11.00 a.m. Bath–Evercreech junction goods train at the mouth of Combe Down tunnel after having assisted up the 2 miles of 1 in 50 gradient out of Bath. This view was taken from the brake van on 5.9.60.

S&D class 7F 2–8–0 No. 53804 of Bath shed passing Midford with a 'Down' freight on 19.8.59. The line at this point is on the ledge of a hillside.

S&D class 7F 2–8–0 No. 53808, now preserved on the West Somerset Railway, and BR Standard class 5MT 4–6–0 No. 73051 south of Midford with the 10.28 a.m. Manchester–Bournemouth West on 15.8.59.

An interesting variety of locomotive power: ex-LMS goods engine and an SR passenger engine. Class 4F 0–6–0 No. 44424 pilots No. 34102 *Lapford* on the 'Down' Pines Express on 15.8.59, climbing the 1 in 60 gradient and passing BR Standard class 4 2–6–0 waiting with an 'Up' train at the Midford outer home signal for the single line to be cleared.

BR Standard class 4MT 4–6–0 No. 75073 south of Midford with the 4.35 p.m. Bath–Evercreech junction on 10.9.60.

Rebuilt 'West Country' Pacific No. 34042 *Dorchester* with a 'Down' train of Eastern Region coaches near Midford 'Up' distant signal on 2.6.62.

Ex-LMS class 4F 0–6–0 No. 44417 and BR Standard class 5MT No. 73051 head the Pines Express south of Wellow on 21.6.58.

Two class 4F 0–6–0s Nos. 44417 and 44422 near Shoscombe and Single Hill with the 4.35 p.m. Bath–Templecombe on 31.7.59.

Ex-S&D class 4F 0–6–0 No. 44557 and 'West Country' 4–6–2 No. 34041 *Wilton* with a 'Down' express south of Wellow on 21.6.58.

'West Country' class Pacific No. 34040 *Crewkerne* and BR Standard class 5MT 4–6–0 No. 73051 pass Home Farm Viaduct, near Shoscombe, with the 'Down' Pines Express on 20.6.59.

Ex-S&D class 7F 2–8–0 No. 53808, now preserved on the West Somerset Railway, with an 'Up' goods, passes the level crossing at Radstock on 14.8.59. On summer Saturdays particularly this crossing caused serious traffic hold-ups, and even if it was open to road traffic the level crossing over the Bristol to Frome line just to the left may have been closed.

Class 3F 0–6–0T No. 47496 banks the 11.00 a.m. Bath–Evercreech junction goods up the 1 in 50 gradient between Radstock and Midsomer Norton South on 5.9.60. The ex-GWR Bristol to Frome line is right of the smokebox. Hanging on the smokebox door is a hook to enable the guard to uncouple the banker at Masbury Summit without needing to stop the train.

Ex-S&D class 7F 2–8–0 No. 53805 near Midsomer Norton South on 5.9.60 with a 'Down' goods, passing the 1.50 p.m. Evercreech junction–Bath freight. The guard's look-out ducket can be seen lower centre.

BR Standard class 5MT 4–6–0 No. 73047 waiting at Writhlington starting signal on 5.9.60 with the 11.00 a.m. Bath–Evercreech junction goods. The colliery is to the left.

S&D class 7F 2–8–0 No. 53805 leaving Midsomer Norton South on 14.8.59 with an 'Up' train of coal from Norton Hill Colliery, only accessible from the 'Down' line.

Driver Newman and his fireman on class 3F 0–6–0T No. 47557 shunting at Norton Hill Colliery on 14.8.59.

S&D class 7F 2–8–0 No. 53803 passes below the ex-GWR's Yatton–Witham East Somerset line at Shepton Mallet on 22.8.57.

BR Standard class 4MT 2–6–0 No. 76065 on 28.10.61 with the 1.10 p.m. Bournemouth West–Bath Green Park crossing the ex-GWR's West of England line between Bruton and Castle Cary. Western Region coaching stock was generally provided for S&D services around this period.

BR Standard class 4MT 4–6–0 No. 75071 of Bath Green Park shed calls at Wincanton on 4.7.59 with a Bath–Bournemouth West stopping train. Notice the fitted van on the 'Up' line which has been detached from an 'Up' train. As soon as the 'Down' train has been cleared, the shunter will release its brakes to let the van roll back down the gradient across into the goods yard on the 'Down' side.

John Cornelius

Driver Harry Starkey on BR Standard class 5MT 4–6–0 No. 73047 on 5.9.60 at Evercreech junction heading the 1.50 p.m. freight from Evercreech junction to Bath.

Class 3F 0–6–0 No. 43436 sets off from Wincanton with a Highbridge–Templecombe local on 4.7.59.

John Cornelius

S&D class 7F 2–8–0 No. 53808 of Bath shed, now preserved on the West Somerset Railway, on the turntable at Templecombe on 31.7.61.

John Cornelius

Class 2P 4–4–0 No. 40537 at Templecombe shed on 31.7.61 awaiting a turn of duty.

John Cornelius

A variety of locomotives at Templecombe on 22.7.57: S&D class 7F 2–8–0 No. 53800 and class 2MT 2–6–2T No. 41296 in the goods yard, while 'West Country' Pacific No. 34108 *Wincanton* passes with a 'Down' express. The locomotive shed is the modernistic-looking building on the far left. The fence posts are made from old lengths of rail.

R.E. Toop

Operation of S&D passenger trains at Templecombe was interesting as a reversal was necessary either into or out of the platform. Here BR Standard class 9F 2–10–0 No. 92224, working the 4.13. p.m. Evercreech junction–Bournemouth West, after calling at Templecombe, has been drawn back to Templecombe junction and sets off southwards on 24.8.63.

S.P.J.A. Derek

Class 3F 0–6–0 No. 43734 of Templecombe shed arrives at Evercreech junction with a goods train from Highbridge on 31.8.60. A backing signal, X-shaped, is to the right of the smokebox.

Class 3F 0–6–0 No. 43682 leaves Pylle with the 1.20 p.m. Evercreech junction–Burnham-on-Sea on 4.7.59. The signal-box was reduced to a ground frame in 1929.

R.E. Toop

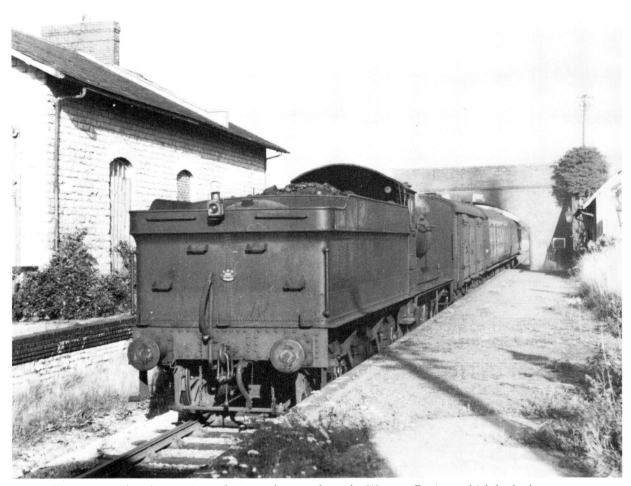

Three years after the previous photograph was taken, the Western Region, which had taken over operating the S&D, replaced ex-LMS engines with those of the GWR. Here 2251 class 0–6–0 No. 3215 leaves Pylle with the 6.02 p.m. Evercreech junction–Highbridge on 21.8.62. The loco carries the GWR headcode for a stopping train, rather than that indicating an S&D passenger train.

Class 3F 0–6–0 No. 43436 enters West Pennard with the 9.55 a.m. Evercreech junction–Highbridge on 22.8.59.

R.E. Toop

Ex-GWR 2251 class 0–6–0 No. 2247 leaving Glastonbury and Street with the 1.20 p.m. Evercreech junction–Highbridge on 13.4.63. The tor can be seen on the skyline.

R.E. Toop

No. 2204 of the same class leaves Glastonbury with the 4.00 p.m. Highbridge–Templecombe on 16.6.62. At the rear of the cab roof a tarpaulin can be seen. This is rolled back to the tender when working tender-first to afford a certain amount of shelter to the crew. The 'goal post' at the front of the tender was fitted by BR to ex-GWR tenders to prevent firemen from striking overhead electric wires with fire irons. This problem did not arise with ex-LMS tenders which generally had doors.

R.E. Toop

Class 4F 0–6–0 No. 44272 arrives at Bason Bridge on 18.5.63 to pick up milk tanks from the Wilts United Dairies, the building of which can be seen in the background. In the foreground is the River Brue.

R.E. Toop

Highbridge on 28.4.62 looking over the railway level crossing towards Burnham-on-Sea. Class 3F 0–6–0 No. 43216 with a transfer freight is about to gain access to the ex-GWR Bristol to Taunton main line. To the left of the photograph is the ex-GWR Highbridge crossing signal-box.

John Cornelius

Having deposited its train on ex-GWR metals, class 3F 0–6–0 No. 43216 returns to S&D territory on 28.4.62.

John Cornelius

Latterly the S&D station at Highbridge was over-platformed, five being excessive for the traffic. On the wet afternoon of 13.4.63, ex-GWR 2251 class 0–6–0 No. 3216 waits at platform 3 with the 2.20 p.m. to Templecombe. In the distance to the right can be seen the engine shed and the buildings of the former S&D loco works.

Leaking steam on 13.4.63, ex-GWR 2251 class 0–6–0 No. 3216 stands at Highbridge platform 3 heading the 2.20 p.m. Highbridge–Templecombe.

A busy scene at Highbridge on a brighter day, 22.6.63. On the right the 1.15 p.m. from Evercreech junction has recently arrived behind 2251 class 0–6–0 No. 2204, while in the background the 2.20 p.m. to Evercreech junction departs behind No. 3210 of the same class.

S.P.J.A. Derek

Class 3F 0–6–0 No. 43427 of Templecombe shed runs round the 1.20 p.m. Evercreech junction–Burnham-on-Sea at the terminus on 22.8.59. On the right is the excursion platform for use on days when long specials were run in addition to regular services. Although Burnham closed to general traffic on 29.10.51, regular excursions were ran until 8.9.62.

R.E. Toop

43XX class 2–6–0 No. 6384 waits to depart from Weston-super-Mare General on 13.9.58 with the 2.15 p.m. Taunton–Bristol Temple Meads, while 'Castle' class 4–6–0 No. 5047 *Earl of Dartmouth* enters with a 'Down' express. The platforms are lit by gas lamps. The bracket signals just to the right of No. 6384 are 'Up' starting signals from Locking Road station.

R.E. Toop

Ex-War Department 2–8–0 No. 90315 passes Uphill junction with a 'Down' express freight on 18.5.57. The lines to Weston-super-Mare curve left and above, Worlebury Hill can be seen in the distance. The loop was singled in 1972.

R.E. Toop

57XX class 0–6–0PT No. 9647 passes Highbridge on the 'Down' line on 13.4.63. The S&D level crossing can be seen immediately behind the brake van.

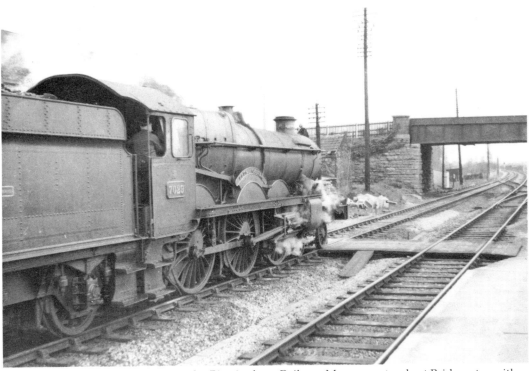

4–6–0 No. 7029 *Clun Castle*, now at the Birmingham Railway Museum, stands at Bridgwater with a Bristol–Paignton train on 15.4.63.

John Cornelius

45XX class 2–6–2T No. 5563 at Durston with a brake van branded 'Castle Cary RU', the 'RU' standing for 'Reserved User' and indicating that the vehicle was not for general use, but only by the named depot. A dmu enters with the noon Saturdays-only Bristol Temple Meads–Taunton on 2.6.62.

R.E. Toop

5101 class 2–2–6T No. 4143 leaves Durston on 8.6.63 with the 5.55 p.m. Taunton–Yeovil Pen Mill. Note that the 'B' headlamp is carried centrally on the buffer beam, understandably as the correct position on the bunker involved some physical effort from the fireman. Good examples of modern GWR tubular metal signal posts can be seen.

S.P.J.A. Derek

45XX class 2–6–2T No. 5548 enters Durston on 2.6.62 with the 4.00 p.m. Yeovil Pen Mill–Taunton carrying the 'B' headlamp in the orthodox position. The leading vehicle was designed by Hawksworth.

R.E. Toop

BR Standard class 3MT 2–6–2T No. 82042 arrives at Durston on 8.6.63 with the 5.45 p.m. Yeovil Pen Mill–Taunton. Notice the comprehensive nameboard, the mixture of breeze blocks and bricks for the platform wall, the unusual rectangular plan signal-box, and the World War Two 'pill box' on top of the cutting. This latter was part of a line of defences stretching from the River Parrett to Seaton with the object of containing the Germans had they invaded the south-western peninsula, thus preventing them from spreading to the rest of the country.

S.P.J.A. Derek

4–6–0 No. 5998 *Trevor Hall* on 6.8.61 heads a 'Down' express from Bristol, the leading coach being of LNER origin. It has crossed the Castle Cary line by a flying junction. Being a Sunday, Cogload junction signal-box was switched out.

John Cornelius

4–6–0 No. 6803 *Bucklebury Grange* with a three thousand gallon tender on 5.8.61, passing over Creech troughs with a 'Down' express, the first coaches of which are composed of Eastern Region stock.

John Cornelius

At Taunton the fireman of No. 6940 *Didlington Hall* shovels the coal forward on 2.9.61. The fact that this Kingswear train is standing on the 'Down' main line just outside the station indicates that a crew change is about to take place. A Bulleid coach is marshalled behind the tender.

John Cornelius

4–6–0 No. 6995 *Benthall Hall* on 'Up' side carriage pilot duty at Taunton on 14.5.60. No. 6995 was considered to be one of Taunton shed's best 'Halls' and was claimed to run like a sewing machine from one work's visit to the next, unlike its sisters which could run roughly as mileage accummulated.

John Cornelius

57XX class 0–6–0PT No. 7713 of Taunton shed on 'Up' side carriage pilot duty at its home station on 16.4.60. It was rather unusual to sport 'A' headlamps on a shunting turn!

John Cornelius

4–6–0 No. 5098 *Clifford Castle* at Taunton with a 'Down' train on 23.4.60.

John Cornelius

'Warship' class diesel-hydraulic No. D804 *Avenger* stands at the middle platform at Taunton on 24.12.59 with a Plymouth–Paddington train, while 45XX class 2–6–2T No. 5571 stands on the 'Up' relief line with a morning service to Yeovil Pen Mill.

John Cornelius

BR Standard class 7MT No. 70020 *Mercury* arrives at Taunton with a Saturdays-only Cardiff–Kingswear train on 9.7.61.

John Cornelius

43XX class 2–6–0 No. 6372, with snow on its tender, threads the layout west of Taunton station on 31.12.62 during the Big Freeze.

John Cornelius

Ex-works 4–6–0 No. 7916 *Mobberley Hall* approaches Taunton with an 'Up' express freight on 31.12.62.

John Cornelius

A visiting SR class U 2–6–0 No. 31798 scurries along the 'Up' main line near Creech St Michael on 6.8.61 returning light engine to Yeovil after working an excursion from Yeovil to Taunton and Paignton via the branch. Creech 'Down' distant signals can be seen to the right.

John Cornelius

45XX class 2–6–2T No. 4567 heads an afternoon Taunton–Castle Cary stopping passenger train near Cogload junction on 29.7.60.

John Cornelius

4–6–0 No. 4992 *Crosby Hall* hurries a Paddington-bound train over Curry Rivel junction on 18.6.60. The branch to Yeovil is on the left.

John Cornelius

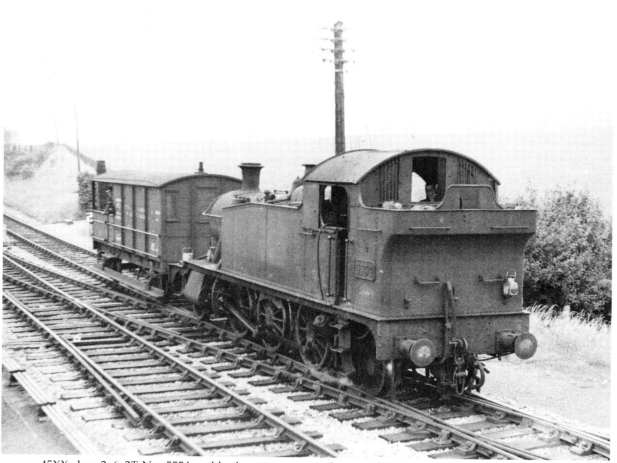

45XX class 2–6–2T No. 5554 and brake van appear to have had little business on 18.6.60 with the Yeovil–Taunton pick-up freight. Before joining the main line at Curry Rivel junction, the daily can of water for the junction signalman has to be delivered. This can be seen on the loco's front buffer beam.

John Cornelius

45XX class 2–6–2T No. 4567 is side-tracked in the 'Up' siding at Curry Rivel junction with an afternoon Taunton–Castle Cary local on 6.6.60. This procedure was adopted to allow two Paddington-bound trains to overtake.

John Cornelius

BR Standard class 3MT 2–6–2T No. 82044 at Langport East on 21.8.62 with the 5.00 p.m. Taunton–Castle Cary.

43XX class 4–6–0 No. 7326 of Taunton heads the 11.15 a.m. to Barnstaple junction on 9.8.63. On the left, diesel-hydraulic No. D1039 *Western King* stands on the main line. No. 7326 was built with side windows and a screw reverser in 1932 as No. 9304. It had a heavy weight behind the buffer beam so that the pony truck would impart more side thrust to the main frames and bear a greater share of flange wear on severely curved routes. It was classified red. By 1956 scrapping of earlier engines caused a shortage of 'blue' engines and so the 93XX series had their weights removed in 1956–9 and were renumbered.

43XX class 2–6–0 No. 7337, formerly No. 9315, of Taunton, about to enter the single line at Morebath junction on 8.6.63. It is working the 10.50 a.m. Barnstaple junction–Taunton train.

61XX class 2–6–2T No. 6113 on 24.4.62 with the 3.12. p.m. Taunton–Minehead crosses an 'Up' train at Williton. When new in the thirties, this class worked in the London division, but twenty years later some were drafted to the provinces.

R.E. Toop

61XX class 2–6–2T No. 6115 with the 1.23 p.m. Minehead–Taunton crosses a 'Down' train at Williton on 24.4.62.

R.E. Toop

45XX class 2–6–2T No. 4591 waits to leave Langport West on 12.5.64 with the 16.00 Yeovil Pen Mill–Taunton service. Notice pedestrians dangerously crossing the line ahead of the engine despite the footbridge and probably a warning notice.

John Cornelius

45XX class 2–6–2T No. 5525 arrives at flooded Langport West station on 29.10.60 with a morning train from Yeovil Pen Mill–Taunton. The line at this location was flooded many times during its history due to the close proximity of the River Parrett.

John Cornelius

61XX class 2–6–2T No. 6146 of Exeter shed leaves Thorney and Kingsbury Halt on 25.1.62 with the 9.50 a.m. Taunton–Yeovil Pen Mill train.

John Cornelius

45XX class 2–6–2T No. 4591 leaves Thorney & Kingsbury Halt on 27.5.64 with the 4.20 p.m. Taunton to Yeovil. The smokebox number plate and shed plate have been removed, either by souvenir hunters, or to prevent their being stolen by such people who were prevalent in the last days of steam. The siding in the foreground served the dairy of Nesmilk Ltd.

John Cornelius

Signalman Tom Howell at Martock exchanges staffs on 16.5.64 with the driver of BR Standard class 3MT 2–6–2T No. 82044 working a Yeovil Pen Mill–Taunton train three weeks before the branch closed. Notice the coal bunker sprinklers actually at work spraying the coal to keep the dust down.

John Cornelius

74XX class 0–6–0PT No. 7436 approaching Martock on 21.8.62 with a pick-up freight from Yeovil. The white post in the foreground is used for holding a staff ready for collection by a fireman.

5101 class 2–6–2T No. 4103 east of Montacute on 21.8.62 with the 9.45 a.m. Taunton to Yeovil. No headlamp is apparent.

57XX class 0–6–0PT No. 4612, now at Swindon Railway Engineering Ltd, is leaving Ilminster with the 2.42 p.m. Taunton–Chard Central on 27.5.61.

R.E. Toop

57XX class 0–6–0PT No. 3787 approaching Chard junction on 21.8.62 with the 3.15 p.m. from Taunton.

57XX class 0–6–0PT No. 4622 pulls up for water at Chard Central on 18.8.62 after working the 12.45 p.m. Chard junction–Chard Central. Sister engine No. 4663, working a freight turn, waits in the bay platform with ex-GWR slip coach No. W7375W. This 1948 Hawksworth vehicle and two others were converted to slip coaches from brake compos as recently as 1958 for use on the remaining Western Region slip services. Following the ending of this form of working, the very last in the world, at Bicester on 9.9.60, still in their chocolate and cream livery, these three coaches with slip gear removed, were transferred to Taunton for use on local stopping services. The train shed can be seen left.

S.P.J.A. Derek

57XX class 0–6–0PT No. 8783 on 25.8.62 with the letters 'GWR' still visible on the side of its tank 14½ years after nationalization, uncouples at Chard junction after working the 6.09 p.m. Chard Central–Chard junction.

S.P.J.A. Derek

On a wet August Bank Holiday Monday, 6.8.62, 57XX class 0–6–0PT No. 9670 arrives at the branch platform, Chard junction, with the 11.00 a.m. special excursion from Taunton–Seaton and Lyme Regis. Due to the appalling weather, loading was light and only three coaches were taken from Chard junction onwards to the coast, the other three being left at Chard junction to await the return working that evening. This was the last BR excursion over the branch.

S.P.J.A. Derek

Class S15 4–6–0 No. 30831 enters Chard junction with the 3.34 p.m. Templecombe–Exeter on 21.8.62.

Class N 2–6–0 No. 31855 speeds through Chard junction on 18.8.62 with the Saturdays-only Exmouth and Sidmouth–Cleethorpes through train which will run from Templecombe over the S&D line to Bath. The rolling stock of this train was not used intensively. It arrived at Exmouth one Saturday and was retained until its return seven days later. The Chard branch platform is to the right of the signal-box.

S.P.J.A. Derek

Rebuilt 'West Country' class Pacific No. 34048 *Crediton* makes an impressive start from Chard junction on 24.2.62 with an Exeter–Yeovil stopping train.

John Cornelius

'Schools' class 4–4–0 No. 30925 *Cheltenham*, now owned by the National Railway Museum, approaches Crewkerne with an Exeter–Yeovil stopping train on 2.9.62.

John Cornelius

BR Standard class 4MT 2–6–0 No. 76066 eases out of the 'Up' sidings at Chard junction on 30.4.62 with a pick-up freight for Yeovil. To the left is the Wilts United Dairies milk depot and its own Ruston and Hornsby four-wheeled shunter which worked there until 1976 when it was transferred to the West Somerset Railway.

John Cornelius

Class S15 4–6–0 No. 30845 heads an Exmouth junction–Nine Elms freight away from Chard junction on 19.3.61.

John Cornelius

'Battle of Britain' Pacific No. 34079 *141 Squadron* arrives at snowbound Crewkerne with a stopping train from Exeter on 7.1.63.

John Cornelius

Rebuilt 'Merchant Navy' Pacific No. 35004 *Cunard White Star* arrives at Crewkerne on 7.1.63 with a semi-fast to Exeter Central during the Big Freeze. The van to the right of the smokebox is a calf box.

John Cornelius

'West Country' Pacific No. 34091 *Weymouth* hurries the 10.30 a.m. Exeter Central–Waterloo through Crewkerne on 7.1.63.

John Cornelius

'Battle of Britain' Pacific No. 34084 *253 Squadron* calls at Crewkerne with a stopping train on 7.1.63. Notice the permanent-way gang employed on keeping the points clear of snow. This new signal-box was opened on 6.11.60 and closed on 26.2.67.

John Cornelius

Class S15 4–6–0 No. 30827 heads an engineer's special on 2.9.62 carrying sections of permanent way through Crewkerne heading for Yeovil junction. The large tender is very apparent in this view.

John Cornelius

'Battle of Britain' Pacific No. 34062 *17 Squadron* heads away from Yeovil junction for Salisbury on 25.7.59. The line to the right of the smokebox leads to Yeovil Town.

John Cornelius

'Battle of Britain' Pacific No. 34061 *73 Squadron* waits for the road at Yeovil junction on 3.8.60 with an afternoon Templecombe–Exeter Central stopping train.

John Cornelius

Class N15 'King Arthur' 4–6–0 No. 30763 *Sir Bors de Ganis* leaves Yeovil junction on 25.7.59 with a summer Saturday extra for Waterloo.

John Cornelius

Rebuilt 'West Country' class Pacific No. 34095 *Brentor* arrives at Yeovil junction on 15.1.63 with the 9.00 a.m. Waterloo–West of England express while sister engine No. 34048 *Crediton* waits in a siding to following later with a stopping train to Exeter Central. The Big Freeze was still continuing.

John Cornelius

Rebuilt 'West Country' class Pacific No. 34031 *Torrington* leaves Yeovil junction with a Waterloo train on 25.7.59.

John Cornelius

'Merchant Navy' class Pacific No. 35006 *Peninsular & Oriental S.N. Co.*, now preserved by the Gloucestershire Warwickshire Railway, approaches Yeovil junction on 25.7.59 with a Waterloo–West of England train on one of its last workings in its original form. By 3.8.59 it was in Eastleigh Works for rebuilding.

John Cornelius

This scene is typical of steam days and a contrast to the clean countryside beyond. 57XX class 0–6–0PT No. 9647 leaves Yeovil Town with the 11.21 a.m. Yeovil Pen Mill–Taunton on 18.5.63. At the adjacent platform a WR pannier tank with auto trailers has displaced the SR class M7 0–4–4T with push-pull set which formerly worked the shuttle service to Yeovil junction. Yeovil MPD is on the right.

S.P.J.A. Derek

Class U 2–6–0 No. 31798 leaves its home shed, Yeovil Town, to take up a turn of duty on 28.10.61.

John Cornelius

Having worked a train from Exeter, 'Schools' class 4-4-0 No. 30937 *Epsom* from Ashford (Kent) shed prepares to go on shed at Yeovil Town on 18.10.61. The 'Schools' class was transferred to the Salisbury to Exeter line about 1959 following the introduction of dmu's on the Hastings line. The fact that Yeovil Town was a joint station explains the GWR signal-box visible above the boiler. The Western Region passenger service stopped using the station in 1964 when Yeovil Pen Mill–Taunton trains were withdrawn. Southern Region branch trains from Yeovil Town–Yeovil junction ceased in 1966. From then until complete closure in 1967, the station was only used as a parcels depot.

John Cornelius

'West Country' class Pacific No. 34091 *Weymouth* about to go on shed at Yeovil Town on 18.10.61.
John Cornelius

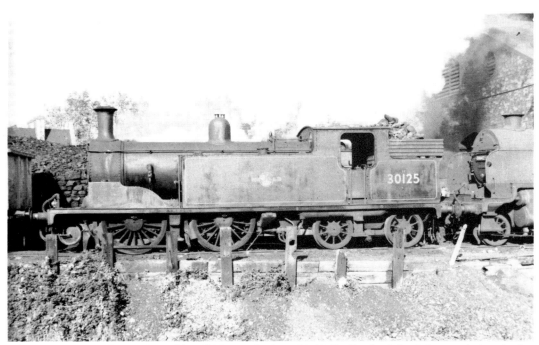

Class M7 0–4–4T No. 30125 at Yeovil Town shed on 28.10.61. To the left of the smokebox is the shed's coalstack, some of which has been used to coal the M7, lumps even being placed on the cab roof. Behind the bunker is class N 2–6–0 No. 31842.

John Cornelius

'Schools' class 4–4–0 No. 30913 *Christ's Hospital* calls at Templecombe on 31.7.61 with an afternoon stopping service to Salisbury. The first coach is still painted in 'blood and custard' livery. S&D trains called at a platform situated under the right-hand end of the canopy.

John Cornelius

Class N 2–6–0 No. 31835 of Exmouth junction shed arrives at Templecombe in ex-works condition on 31.7.61 with a 'Down' fitted freight.

John Cornelius

Rebuilt 'Merchant Navy' class Pacific No. 35012 *United States Line* approaches Templecombe on 20.7.57 with an 'Up' express.

R.E. Toop

Shedman Ernie Caulley raises an arm to acknowledge the last tub of coal tipped on the tender of the last locomotive to be serviced at Templecombe before the shed's closure on 6.3.66. 'Merchant Navy' Pacific No. 35028 *Clan Line*, now owned by Southall Railway Centre, is being prepared to work the final railtour from the 'Dorset' back to Waterloo.

John Cornelius

57XX class 0–6–0PT No. 9732 and 2251 class 0–6–0 No. 2268 double head a train to Weymouth under the twin bridges just east of Yeovil junction station on 25.7.59. The SR main line is carried on the steel girder bridge, while the stone-built occupation bridge was a Mecca for spotters in steam days. No. 9732 assisted up the 1 in 51 ruling gradient to Evershot 8½ miles distant and then returned to Yeovil Pen Mill for further duties.

John Cornelius

53XX class 2–6–0 No. 6344 rounds curves near Yeovil junction with a Bristol–Weymouth express on 25.7.59. The embankment on the left carries the Yeovil junction to Yeovil Town branch line.

John Cornelius

4–6–0 No. 6997 *Bryn-Ivor Hall* about to leave Yeovil Pen Mill on 31.7.61 with a Bristol–Weymouth stopping train. A dmu stands on the other road which is served by two platforms, an unusual layout which facilitated the transfer of passengers to and from the Yeovil Town and Taunton branch trains.

John Cornelius

Peckett 0–6–0ST works No. 1041, built 1906, *Lord Salisbury*, at Norton Hill Colliery, Midsomer Norton, on 14.8.59.

Industrial railways were not always in a bleak and depressing setting. Parts of the Kilmersdon Colliery line near Radstock were idyllic. Peckett 0–4–0ST, Works No. 1788, built 1929, shunting at the head of the incline down to the Bristol to Frome branch on 6.6.68. Following closure of the colliery in 1973, the loco has been preserved on the West Somerset Railway.

View from the cab of Peckett No. 1788 travelling between the incline and the colliery on 6.6.68.

Peckett No. 1788 shunting at Kilmersdon Colliery on 5.11.68.

Another line with idyllic sections was the ARC 2 mile long railway through Vallis Vale near Frome, between the Radstock to Frome line and Whatley Quarry. It was worked by Sentinel geared locos which had the general appearance of diesel engines and with their fast revving engines, also had their sound. The vertical boiler was concealed in the cab, while the bonnet contained cylinders and gearing. In this view, No. 1 is ascending the gradient towards the Bristol to Frome (North Somerset) branch line on 5.11.68.

Following the replacement of the steam locomotives by diesels on the section to Whatley Quarry, No. 1 was kept for shunting in the exchange sidings close to the BR line. Coupled diesel units Nos. 2 and 3 have just arrived with a loaded train on 5.11.68.

No. 1 on BR track after having taken the foreman to Somerset Stone Quarries Siding South ground frame. Diesel-hydraulic No. D7002 approaching from Frome with empty ballast wagons on 5.11.68.

No. 1 shunting in the exchange sidings situated in a sylvan setting on 5.11.68.

In its last years, the S&D saw many steam specials. Ex-GWR 43XX class 2–6–0 No. 6384 is an unusual visitor to the Mangotsfield to Bath line on 14.5.60 as it approaches Bath junction with the Ian Allan Severn–Wessex Express.

On arrival at Bath Green Park, No. 6384 was detached and an ex-S&D class 7F 2–8–0 attached to the other end to work it over the S&D. Here No. 53807 tackles the 1 in 50 gradient beyond Bath junction on 14.5.60 while the fireman leans out to retrieve the single-line tablet from the catcher.

Class 8F 2–8–0 No. 48309, not normally used for S&D passenger duties, works the Locomotive Club of Great Britain's Wessex Downsman rail tour by Bath junction on 2.5.65.

Two ex-S&D locos, class 7F 2–8–0 No. 53807 and class 4F 0–6–0 No. 44558, pass Bath junction with the Home Counties' Railway Society special on 7.6.64. The fireman of No. 53807 looks out of the cab to check that the 'falling man' type of apparatus, seen near the back of the tender, has correctly collected the tablet from the catcher on the tender.

The Home Counties' Railway Society special left Bath for Cheltenham on 7.6.64 behind ex-GWR 4–6–0 No. 7023 *Penrice Castle*, an unusual visitor to this former LMS line.

'Merchant Navy' class Pacific No. 35028 *Clan Line*, now preserved at Southall Railway Centre, waits outside Templecombe shed on 6.3.66. It was rebuilt in 1951 to work the last rail tour from the northern section of the S&D back to Waterloo.

John Cornelius

Having been hauled from London by LNER Pacific No. 4472 *Flying Scotsman*, the Ian Allan rail tour leaves Taunton for Barnstaple junction behind 43XX class 2–6–0 No. 7332 (No. 9310 until 1958) and No. 7317 on 19.10.63.

John Cornelius

The record-breaking 4–4–0 No. 3440 *City of Truro*, now preserved by the National Railway Museum, at Taunton on a special from Swindon to Kingswear on 19.5.57.

M.E.J. Deane

No. 3440 *City of Truro* at Taunton with the Westward Television exhibition train on an unknown date.

Author's collection

No. 3440 *City of Truro* on the Bristol and North Somerset Railway on 28.4.57 between Bristol and Radstock with the RCTS North Somerset rail tour. It is assisted by 45XX 2–6–2T No. 5528 which in true GWR fashion is placed 'inside' the train engine. No. 5528 is ex-works and painted in the green-lined livery permitted that year to many classes hitherto black or lined black.

G.A. Dando collection

An RCTS special which travelled over goods-only lines in the Bristol Harbour area, is shown here crossing Ashton swing bridge behind a pannier tank on 26.9.59. This bridge has twin decks: the upper carrying a public road and the lower a double track railway. It was turned by hydraulic power.

Dr A.J.G. Dickens/author's collection

SR 'Battle of Britain' class Pacific No. 34079 *141 Squadron* about to leave Bristol Temple Meads on 14.6.64 with the Derbyshire Railway Society special visit to Derby and Crewe works. This type of locomotive worked to Bristol on football specials when teams in the SR area were playing a Bristol team.

Hugh Ballantyne

Rebuilt 'West Country' Pacific No. 34018 *Axminster* at Westmoreland Road goods yard, Bath, *en route* to the scrap yard on 19.2.68.

Main-line steam on BR did not quite come to an end in August 1968, for although it had no steam locos, it still possessed quite a number of steam-operated cranes including this 145-ton machine depicted at Bath Road diesel depot, Bristol, on 29.7.80.